AM 20

Jarrold Caterpillars Series Book 3
With Text and Photographs by
George E. Hyde

British

barcode

D1789168

978 0857067306

Caterpillars

Moths Book 2

Jarrold Colour Publications, Norwich

As explained in the two previous books of this series on caterpillars, the caterpillar stage is the growing period in the life cycle of moths and butterflies. More hawk moth caterpillars are included here, and a further selection of eggar and tiger moths. There are also some species belonging to the Noctuae, and more examples of 'Loopers' as the caterpillars of the geometer moths are known.

Many who are interested in moths and butterflies rear the caterpillars at home, but to do this successfully requires knowledge of the respective food-plants. While it is true that some species of caterpillars have catholic tastes, and thrive on a variety of plants, many are restricted to single kinds of plants. So whenever you collect caterpillars in the wild, and take them home for rearing, note carefully the kinds of plants on which they are feeding, and give your captives the same. Another important rule is to see that only fresh leaves are offered to the caterpillars. To maintain freshness the stems of the leaves, or flowers (some caterpillars eat flowers), should be plugged into small bottles containing water. Cotton wool packed round the stems will prevent the caterpillars entering and drowning – a common happening if this rule is neglected.

In addition to rearing caterpillars in cages, plastic boxes are useful for keeping some small species, but it is important not to crowd them, also to clean out the boxes every day, carefully removing withered leaves and other debris including droppings. Yet another popular method is to 'sleeve' the caterpillars on to growing food-plants. This is especially useful when they feed on such trees as oak, birch, or poplar growing in one's own garden. For obvious reasons young trees with low branches are best for this purpose. The actual 'sleeve' is a long cylinder made of muslin or similar material. One end is slipped over a convenient spray of leaves, and firmly

◄1. **Convolvulus Hawk** (*Herse convolvuli*) 90–96 mm. The Convolvulus Hawk moth has a wing-span of over 100 mm, but although a regular visitor to Britain it is not a native. It has an unusually long proboscis which exceeds the length of its body, and this is illustrated in Book 1 of the series on moths. The majority of the moths are found near the coast, but some travel far inland and are attracted by bright street lights. Caterpillars are also found occasionally, and are eagerly sought by moth-collectors. They vary in colour from apple-green with brown and black markings, to much deeper colours like the one illustrated here. The red-brown pupa is inside a frail silken cocoon. The caterpillars feed on bindweed and other species of convolvulus. One that we reared pupated in September and the moth emerged in October.

tied on to the stem. The caterpillars are then placed inside, and the free end of the 'sleeve' is also securely fastened with string. If the last detail is neglected predatory insects, including earwigs, may find their way in and kill the caterpillars.

Sleeves should be examined every two days or so, and when the leaves are all eaten they must be removed to new sprays. Some caterpillars, including those that spin cocoons in which to pupate, can be left inside the 'sleeves' until they are fully grown, but species that burrow into the ground before making the change should be moved to flower-pots containing fine soil or granulated peat in which to pupate. Most pupae remain healthy if they are stored on damp moss, and not exposed to bright sunshine which can kill them. Some caterpillars that burrow into soil do not pupate immediately, but live for several weeks before making the change. They should not be disturbed. Most of the pupae enclosed in cocoons are also better if left undisturbed, but some rearers carefully remove them before the moths are due to hatch out.

All newly emerged moths and butterflies have small, limp wings, and it requires an hour or more for these to reach full size. In the wild the insects hang from twigs or leaves during this critical time, but in captivity they often remain suspended from the roof or sides of the cages. They must not be disturbed or their wings may not expand properly. If any specimens reared in this way are required for a collection they should be killed in a humane way, but many who breed moths and butterflies at home release them. This is all to the good, but it is important that the various species concerned are given their liberty in places where they are normally found. If, for example, woodland haunting moths are released in a town they are in danger of coming to grief, and the effort of rearing them is wasted.

Many people form collections of moths and butterflies, and if this is in moderation little harm is done, but it is not in the scope of the present work to include details of the best methods to follow, nor to refer to the ethics of the subject. Anyone seeking detailed information will find helpful literature on how to preserve the specimens for a collection. As in the companion books of the series, this one contains pictures from colour photographs of living caterpillars, and there are also informative details in the accompanying text. Following modern practice the average length of the subjects is given in millimetres, but bear in mind that a walking caterpillar usually looks longer than when it is resting. Many of the figures are enlarged to make the details more obvious to readers.

Poplar Hawk moth life cycle

Moths and butterflies go through four distinct stages of development before they reach maturity. The stages are egg (ovum), caterpillar (larva), pupa or chrysalis and imago. The transformation is known as a complete metamorphosis. The five pictures show the development of a Poplar Hawk (*Laothoe populi*) from egg to moth.

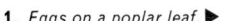 *1. Eggs on a poplar leaf.* ▶

2. Caterpillar.

3. Two Pupae.

4. Male Moth drying wings.

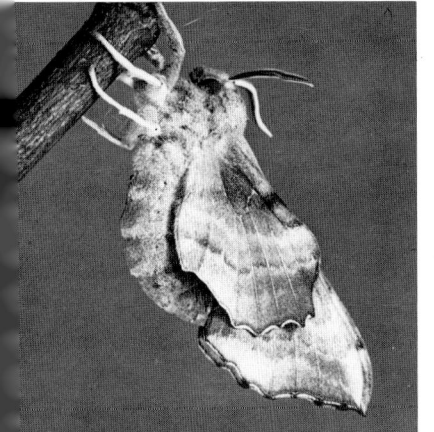

5. Female Moth.

2. **Small Elephant Hawk** (*Deilephila porcellus*) 38–45 mm. The Small Elephant Hawk moth is illustrated in Book 4 of the series on moths, and a pale form of the caterpillar is also shown. The species is widely distributed in England and its range extends into Scotland, but it is less common than the larger species of elephant hawk moth. The caterpillars feed on lady's bedstraw and related plants including white bedstraw. A dark example of the caterpillar is shown here. The pupa is enclosed in a loose cocoon of silk and earth.

3. **Sallow Kitten** (*Harpyia furcula*) 30 mm. The Sallow Kitten, a small relation of the well-known Puss moth, belongs to the family Notodontidae. Although not usually common it is found locally in much of Britain, and is on the wing in June. It flies by night and is attracted by bright lights. The black, button-shaped eggs are laid on sallow or willow leaves, and the caterpillars can be found in late summer. The pupa is inside a tough cocoon which is usually spun on bark.

4. **Great Prominent** (*Notodonta trepida-anceps*) 50 mm. The Great Prominent, as its name implies, is larger than most species of prominent moths. Its brownish-grey fore wings lack bright colours, and its hind wings are whitish. It is commonest in the south of England. When at rest on the trunk of an oak tree it usually matches the bark and is difficult to detect. The green caterpillar has seven oblique stripes on each side. It feeds on oak in July and early August, and when fully grown it burrows into the ground to pupate. The dark pupa is enclosed in a tough earthen cocoon.

2

3

5

6

5. Plumed Prominent (*Ptilophora plumigera*) 28 mm. The Plumed Prominent is so named because of the plume-like antennae of the male. The moth appears in late October and November, and is found in some chalk areas of southern England, especially in Buckinghamshire and Kent. It is occasionally noticed at rest by day, but is seen more often after dark when attracted by a bright light. Eggs are laid on twigs of maple trees, and can be found during the winter by careful searching. They hatch in the spring, and the blue-green caterpillar has a yellowish line along each side. It feeds on maple and will also eat sycamore leaves.

6. Yellow-Horned (*Achlya flavicornis*) 26 mm. The Yellow-Horned belongs to the family Thyatiridae, and can be found in March and April. It is common in many birch woods in Britain, and rests on the trunk, or on a twig, by day. When on bark its greenish-grey colours usually blend with the background and make the moth hard to recognise. The olive-green, black-spotted caterpillar feeds by night on birch leaves, and hides in a folded leaf in the daytime. The pupa is inside a cocoon among dead leaves or other debris on the soil, and the species sometimes passes a second winter before the moth emerges.

7. Dark Tussock (*Dasychira fascelina*) 35 mm. The Dark Tussock moth belongs to the Lymantriidae family, of which the caterpillars are very hairy. It is less common than the Pale Tussock, and is found mainly in northern England and Scotland. It flies by night, but can sometimes be found by day as it rests on heather or other moorland plants. The caterpillar feeds mainly on heather, but will eat sallow and broom.

8. Pale Oak Eggar (*Trichiura crataegi*) 38 mm. The male Pale Oak Eggar is both paler and smaller than the grey-brown female. The species is found mainly in wooded areas or where there are large hedgerows, and is on the wing in late July and August. The males are very lively after dark and can be attracted by bright lights, but the females are more sluggish. The blackish caterpillars vary in appearance, but one common form has cream-yellow markings on the back. Their main food-plants are blackthorn and hawthorn, but they sometimes eat birch or bramble. The pupa is enclosed in a tough, compact cocoon.

9. Oak Eggar (*Lasiocampa quercus*) 70–80 mm. The Oak Eggar moth flies by day, and the males travel far and quickly in their search for the larger females. The species is found in many parts of southern England, and is replaced in northern areas by the very similar Northern Eggar. The moths are on the wing in July, and the females lay their many eggs loosely as they fly over the heather and other undergrowth. The hairy caterpillar hibernates in winter and is fully grown in late spring. The pupa is inside a smooth cocoon shaped like an acorn.

10. Pebble Hook-Tip (*Drepana falcataria*) 18–20 mm. The moths of the family Drepanidae are known as 'Hook-Tips' because their fore wings are pointed and curved downward at the tip. There are six British species, and the Pebble Hook-Tip is the commonest and best known. It is well distributed where birch trees grow commonly and appears on the wing in June. The caterpillar feeds on birch and can be found in August and September. The pupa is inside a cocoon spun on a leaf.

9

10

11

12

11. Oak Hook-Tip (*Drepana binaria*) 18 mm. The Oak Hook-Tip has yellowish-brown wings marked with paler cross-lines. It is commonest in the south of England, but is found northwards to Yorkshire. The moth is on the wing in July and the caterpillar can be found in August and September. Its main haunts are oak woods, and it feeds on oak leaves. When ready to pupate it spins a slight cocoon on a leaf. The pupa remains inside this during the winter.

12. Water Ermine (*Spilosoma urticae*) 28 mm. The Ermine moths and also the Tiger moths belong to the family Arctiidae. The Water Ermine is commonest in East Anglia, but is found sparingly in some other parts of England, and should not be confused with the commoner White Ermine which has more black dots on its pale wings. It flies in June and is active by night, but can sometimes be seen resting in the daytime on plants growing in its marshy haunts. The hairy caterpillar feeds on aquatic plants such as water-mint. The pupa is inside a rather frail cocoon.

13. Ruby Tiger (*Phragmatobia fuliginosa*) 32 mm. The Ruby Tiger is smaller than the well-known Garden Tiger, and is found in much of Britain including Scotland. When the moth is resting its brown fore wings hide the red, black-edged hind wings, but some examples are more brightly marked than others. Many Scottish specimens are entirely blackish with only a trace of red on the hind wings to relieve this. The caterpillar is not as thickly clothed in hairs as some of its relations. It feeds on such common weeds as dock, dandelion, and plantain. The pupa is inside a silken cocoon.

14

15

14. Common Footman (*Lithosia lurideola*) 26 mm. Footmen moths owe their popular title to their narrow, stiff appearance when at rest, and several species are found in Britain. The family is called Lithosiidae, and the Common Footman is the most widely distributed in much of England and parts of Scotland. Its pale lead-grey fore wings have a yellowish stripe along the front edge, and the hind wings are pale yellow. The related Scarce Footman is very similar in appearance, but is a more local species. The dark grey caterpillar feeds on lichen and hibernates during the winter. It becomes fully grown in June and the moth appears in July.

15. Dark Dagger (*Apatele tridens*) 33 mm. Dagger moths, as explained in Book 1 of the series on caterpillars, are so called because of the dagger-like markings on their fore wings. The Dark Dagger moth is so very similar to the Grey Dagger that even experts cannot distinguish them, but the caterpillars are very distinct in appearance. The grey dagger moth and also its caterpillar are illustrated in Book 3 of the series on moths. The Dark Dagger moth flies in June and is widely, though locally, distributed. The caterpillar can be found in late summer on hawthorn and some orchard trees.

16. Knotgrass (*Apatele rumicis*) 31 mm. The Knotgrass moth lacks bright colours and is mainly different shades of grey. It comes out in June and July, but although well distributed it is easily overlooked when resting because of its dark appearance which often matches the surroundings. The hairy caterpillar is more colourful and better known, because it often feeds on garden plants.

17

18

17. Purple Clay (*Diarsia brunnea*) 35 mm. The Purple Clay belongs to the large assortment of moths known as the Noctuidae. It has purplish-brown fore wings which vary in shade, and it flies in late June and July. Although mainly a woodland species it is well distributed in much of Britain, and it sometimes appears in gardens. The red-brown caterpillar has yellowish markings and can be found in the spring with the help of a lamp as it feeds on different low plants, and also on bramble and honeysuckle.

18. Mediterranean Brocade (*Prodenia litura*) 30 mm. The majority of moth caterpillars are not very harmful to cultivated plants as they feed mainly on weeds or on forest trees, but there are exceptions, including the Mediterranean Brocade moth. It is a serious pest on cotton and some other crop plants including tomatoes. Its occasional presence in Britain could be the result of eggs or caterpillars being imported in produce from overseas. Fortunately there are ways of controlling it.

19. Cabbage moth (*Mamestra brassicae*) 35 mm. The Cabbage moth is a sombre species of mainly dark grey and brown in colour. It is widely spread and common in much of Britain, which is unfortunate considering the harmful nature of the caterpillar which feeds on a variety of weeds, and also has a special liking for cabbage. It can be very destructive, and unlike the caterpillar of the 'cabbage butterfly', which feeds externally and is easily detected, it bores into the inner leaves and remains unseen though producing a trail of damage. The shiny red-brown pupa is buried in soil, and is often dug up by gardeners.

20

21

20. Pale Shining Brown (*Polia nitens*) 44 mm. The Pale Shining Brown moth has glossy brown fore wings, but it is not often seen by day. After dark it becomes more lively, and in addition to being attracted by artificial light it responds to the moth-hunter's 'sugar' patches. It flies in July, and the brownish caterpillar can be found in late summer and autumn feeding on different weeds including sow-thistle. Although a local species it is widely distributed in southern and eastern England, also in parts of Scotland. The pupa is buried in the soil.

21. Saxon (*Hyppa rectilinia*) 36 mm. The attractive grey and brown moth called the 'Saxon' is found chiefly in some areas of Scotland as far north as Sutherland. Its English localities are said to be restricted to Cumberland. The moth flies in late May and June, and is keenly sought by moth-collectors. The caterpillar is mainly brown, but varies in shade. It feeds in late summer on bramble, sallow, and some other trees and plants, and hibernates when fully grown.

22. Merveille du Jour (*Griposia aprilina*) 34 mm. Not many British moths are marked with green, but the Merveille du Jour, a woodland species, is one of the few. Its green fore wings have white-edged black markings, and the moth usually blends well when resting on moss-covered bark. Some examples from north Yorkshire and Durham have extra heavy dark markings. The moth flies in October, and is well distributed in Britain including parts of Scotland. The caterpillar feeds on oak, and rests by day in chinks in the bark where it is difficult to detect. The red-brown pupa is buried in soil.

23. Small Angle Shades (*Euplexia lucipara*) 30 mm. The Small Angle Shades, although far from rare, is not as well known as the Large Angle Shades described in Book 1 of the series on moths. Its purple-brown and black wings bear traces of pink, and the moth can be found in June and July. The caterpillar often feeds on bracken, but also eats birch and sallow. It can be a nuisance on garden ferns.

24. Old Lady *(Mormo maura)* 52 mm. The large dusky-winged moth known as the Old Lady was given the title when elderly ladies dressed in more sober style than they do today. It comes out in July and is widely distributed in Britain including parts of Scotland, but it seems to have declined in numbers in some areas in recent years. The caterpillar is marked with different shades of brown, and it feeds on ivy as well as several other plants such as dock. It hibernates in the winter and completes its growth in the spring. The stout pupa is buried in the soil.

25. Small Mottled Willow (*Laphygma exigua*) 20 mm. The Small Mottled Willow moth lacks bright colours, but is prized by moth-collectors because of its rarity in Britain. It comes to us from overseas, and is classed as a serious pest in North America and elsewhere because of the ravages of the brown and olive-green caterpillars which can be very harmful to different crops including maize. Although the species does occasionally breed here, and produce another generation of moths, it has not caused much destruction to crops or in gardens of Britain. When reared in captivity the caterpillars will eat almost any kind of weed.

24

25

26

27

26. Double Line (*Mythimna turca*) 40 mm. The Double Line moth usually has bright red-brown fore wings marked with darker, wavy cross-lines, but some examples have a dull coppery appearance. It is found mainly in the south of England, and the New Forest is a well-known haunt – we were rather surprised to find the species in open country near the coast of north Cornwall. The caterpillar feeds on various grasses and also on wood rush. It usually hibernates during the winter, but in captivity caterpillars sometimes continue feeding and moths develop during the autumn.

27. Flame Wainscot (*Meliana flammea*) 28 mm. The numerous different moths called 'Wainscots' have few bright colours, but are eagerly sought by moth-collectors. They are found mainly in boggy localities, and the narrow-winged Flame Wainscot is no exception for its haunts are reed-grown areas mainly in East Anglia. It flies by night, and the caterpillar which feeds on reed (Phragmites) is also active after dark. It can be found with the help of a lamp, but is easily disturbed and liable to fall off the reeds.

28. Angle-Striped Sallow (*Enargia paleacea*) 33 mm. The attractive Angle-Striped Sallow moth is illustrated in Book 3 of the series on moths. Although local, the species is found in many places including the north Midlands in England, and in parts of Scotland. It comes out in August, and hides by day, but can be attracted by a bright light after dark, also by 'sugar'. The greyish-green caterpillar has a contrasting yellow head, and it feeds by night on birch. In the daytime it hides between leaves fastened together with silk.

29. Orange Upperwing (*Jodia croceago*) 32 mm. The Orange Upperwing is vividly marked on the fore wings with bright orange, and is one of our most attractive night-flying moths. It is locally distributed in the south and the south-west of England, but is apparently rare elsewhere. It flies first in early autumn, hibernates during the winter, then reappears in early spring. Eggs are laid on the twigs of oak trees, and the caterpillars feed there in May and June. The moths can be found on sallow blooms in April.

30. Wormwood Shark (*Cucullia absinthii*) 33 mm. Several medium-sized moths with narrow fore wings are known as 'sharks' because of their streamlined appearance. They rest by day on fences and walls, and are not easy to find because their markings usually harmonise with the background. The Wormwood Shark is smaller than some others of the family, and it used to be mainly a coastal species, but in recent years it has spread into many inland areas. It flies in July, and its caterpillar feeds on the flowers and seeds of wormwood in August and September. It can also be found on mugwort, a rather similar-looking plant.

31. Gold Spangle (*Plusia bractea*) 32 mm. The Gold Spangle is one of the Plusia moths which are noted for metallic markings on the fore wings. It has long been regarded as a northern species, found especially in Scotland and the Lake District of England, but in recent years it has been recorded from some southern areas. Its brown fore wings have bright golden spots. The moth flies in June and July, and is sometimes taken in moth-traps. The bright green caterpillar has white dots, and it feeds mainly on nettles.

30

31

32. Rosy Underwing (*Catocala electa*) 60 mm. The handsome Rosy Underwing is related to the more familiar Red Underwing, a resident, rather similar-looking species, which is described and illustrated in Book 2 of the series on moths. The Rosy Underwing is a rare immigrant to Britain, and very few examples have been recorded, including one caught in Sussex as long ago as 1875. The narrow caterpillar feeds on willow, mainly by night. It rests by day in crevices in the willow bark, and is very difficult to detect.

33 Waved Black (*Parascotia fuliginaria*) 20 mm. The Waved Black moth has dark wings with wavy pale lines, and it is not easily recognised when resting on bark or any other dark surface. It has been found mainly in the London area, but has also appeared further afield in Surrey. It comes out in June and July, and responds to both light and 'sugar'. The blackish caterpillar, marked with orange dots, feeds on fungus growing on rotten wood. Although it hatches in August the caterpillar is not fully grown until the following spring. When reared in captivity the moths are sometimes rather below normal size.

34. Grass Emerald (*Pseudoterpna pruinata*) 26 mm. The attractive green moths called Emeralds belong to the large super-family Geometridae. There are several species of which two are illustrated in Books 2 and 4 of the series on moths. The Grass Emerald is bluish green when newly emerged, but it soon fades to more sober shades of grey. It flies in June and July, and the green, twig-like caterpillar feeds on broom and gorse in late summer, and again in the spring. It matches the twigs and is easily overlooked.

33

34

35. Beautiful Carpet (*Mesoleuca albicillata*) 28 mm. A number of small Geometer moths are known as 'Carpets', but they should not be confused with the still smaller clothes moths that are indoor pests because their caterpillars feed on carpets and some other household furnishings. The Beautiful Carpet merits its name for its cream-white wings are attractively patterned with deep blue and black. It comes out in June and is widely distributed in wooded areas though not usually common. The caterpillar feeds on blackberry and wild raspberry.

36. Yellow-Ringed Carpet (*Entephria flavicinctata*) 15 mm. The Yellow-Ringed Carpet is a northern species found locally in a few rocky areas of England, but more generally in Scotland and some surrounding islands. It flies in August and rests by day on rocks and stones, but is easily disturbed and soon takes flight. When settled on a rock face it provides a good example of camouflage as its mainly grey colour blends well with the background. The caterpillar varies in colour from green to chocolate or red-brown, and it feeds on saxifrage and stonecrop.

37. Winter moth (*Operophtera brumata*) 23 mm. The Winter moth is a notorious pest that is all too well known by gardeners and foresters because its caterpillars live on almost every species of deciduous tree and shrub, both wild and cultivated. The male has thinly scaled grey-brown wings, marked with darker lines, but the female is apterous and can be mistaken for a small spider. The males fly in the evening in December and January in search of the females, which lay their eggs on the trees. The caterpillars hatch in the spring.

36

37

38. White-Spotted Pug (*Eupithecia tripunctata*) 12 mm. The numerous moths called 'Pugs' are small in size, and many have rather narrow fore wings. Some closely resemble other species, especially those that produce melanic forms, so they are not easy to identify in the moth stage, but the caterpillars have more variation both in appearance and habits. About fifty species of pug moths are found in Britain, and although a few are uncommon and confined to limited habitats, others are widespread and common. The caterpillars feed on a wide variety of plants or trees, and some, including the Foxglove Pug and the Toadflax Pug eat flowers in this stage. Others are restricted to bladder campion and great valerian respectively. Although pug moth caterpillars are often numerous they are very subject to the attacks of ichneumon-flies and other insect parasites. On one occasion when nineteen caterpillars of the Valerian Pug were collected for rearing in captivity, all were found to contain larvae of ichneumons and not one moth was reared. The White-Spotted Pug is on the wing in May, and a second generation sometimes develops in July – especially in hot summers. Its wings are grey-brown with a white speck on each fore wing. The caterpillars feed on the flowers and seed-pods of hogweed. Pupae of the second generation live through winter.

39. Lilac Beauty (*Apeira syringaria*) The graceful Lilac Beauty moth is illustrated in Book 4 of the series on moths. It belongs to the assortment of moths called 'Thorns', and comes out in June and July. Though commonest in the south of England it is found as far north as Yorkshire. The strange-looking caterpillar feeds on both honeysuckle and privet, and when fully grown it spins a small silken cocoon suspended from a leaf, or twig, forming a miniature 'hammock' to contain the pupa.

38

40

40. Barred Red (*Ellopia fasciaria*) 25 mm. The typical Barred Red moth has brick-red wings marked with wavy lines, but some examples are grey in appearance, and in a rarer form the red is replaced by green (variety *prasinaria*). The species is found in much of Britain, including Scotland, where pine trees are common, and the moth often rests on the bark by day, but it flies by night and can be attracted by artificial light. The caterpillar feeds on Scots pine and also on larch. When resting on a twig it is easily overlooked as the illustration shows. It lives through the winter and changes into a pupa in spring among fallen pine needles and other debris.